This teaching method can be used ' reading or spelling and understanding i in pronunciation.

As a rule, when two vowels are togetl usually says its own name, for example: as in spies, óa as in load, úe as in sue.

GRAMMAR

The following explanations should help the child to understand grammar and you can ask him or her to make up sentences with a noun, adjective and verb.

A Noun

A noun is a naming word. Instead of saying "please pass me that", we should name the object, for example: dog, bag, box, etc. These are all nouns, so you should say, "please pass me the **bag**".

An Adjective

An adjective describes something. There are different types of dogs, for example: big dogs, small dogs, black dogs, etc. **Big**, **small** and **black** are all adjectives.

The Verb

The verb tells us what something or somebody is doing or has done. The verb is an action word, for example: **jump**, **run**, **laugh**, **cry**, are all verbs. Sentences are made by using the noun, adjective, and verb together, for example: the big dog **jumps**.

for Poppy
Published by Indigo Children's Books Ltd.
46 Dorothy Road, Battersea, London SW11 2JP.
Tel/Fax: 0171 585 0993

Text copyright © 1999 Alan Evans
Illustrations copyright © 1999 Indigo Children's Books Ltd.
ISBN: 1-86140-017-9

Printed in England

Zak the cat likes to lie in the sun. He is up
on the roof of the hen hut, having a sleep.

Len has some milk for Zak. Zak has a
stretch, then jumps down off the roof. He
runs to Len and rubs up against his legs,
with his soft fur.

The sun is setting and it is getting dark.
Zak likes to look for rats and mice when it
is dark. Rats and mice like to look for food
in the dark.

The moon is shining in the sky. It is very bright and Zak's eyes are lit up like stars.

Zak hides in the cow shed. Zak has not seen the rat eating the cow feed. Can you sec the rat?

Zak can hear a scratching noise. He creeps along the wall of the cow shed and sees the rat. Zak leaps at the rat, but the rat is very quick.

The rat runs through a hole in the wall of the cow shed. The hole is very big, so Zak can run after the rat.

Zak and the rat run into the yard. Zak can run very fast. The rat sees the blue tractor in the yard and runs under it.

The rat runs under the gate. Zak is too big to go under the gate. Poor Zak, what is he going to do?

Zak leaps up onto the top of the gate and then jumps down on the other side. Zak looks for the rat, but he cannot see him. The rat has run away.

Zak has had fun. He likes to hunt rats and mice on the farm. Zak will stay up late tonight, but he will have a long sleep in the sun tomorrow!